Piano Exam Pieces

ABRSM Grade 8

Selected from the 2013 & 2014 syllabus

Name

D0490773

Date of exam

Contents

Editor for ABRSM: Richard Jones

Other pieces for Grade 8

132 St. Pancras Way,
London NW1 9NB

Tel: 020-7482-5424
Fax: 020-7482-5434
Email: dot@dotsonline.co.uk
Web: www.dotsonline.co.uk

First published in 2012 by ABRSM (Publishing) Ltd, a wholly owned subsidiary of ABRSM, 24 Portland Place, London W1B 1LU, United Kingdom © 2012 by The Associated Board of the Royal Schools of Music

Music origination by Julia Bovee
Cover by Kate Benjamin & Andy Potts
Printed in England by Headley Brothers Ltd, The Invicta Press, Ashford, Kent

MIX
Paper from responsible sources
FSC™ C109619

Sonata in B

No. 11 from 27 Sonatas

Antonio Soler
(1729–83)

The Catalan composer Antonio Soler studied in Madrid with Domenico Scarlatti, who became a powerful influence on his keyboard music. In 1752 he joined the staff of the monastery at El Escorial, where, in 1757, he was appointed *maestro de capilla*. Today, Soler's reputation rests largely on his 120 keyboard sonatas. At El Escorial in 1772 he gave autograph manuscripts of 27 sonatas to the English musician and collector Lord Fitzwilliam, so that they could be published in England. This was done by Robert Birchall in about 1796. That edition is today in the British Library, and No. 11 is reproduced from it here.

The source contains many inaccuracies, which – since the composer's intention is usually clear – have been corrected by the editor without comment; bb. 90–1 might be played in the more sophisticated form of bb. 36–7.

Source: *XXVII Sonatas para clave* (London: R. Birchall, *c.*1796)

© 2012 by The Associated Board of the Royal Schools of Music

Prelude and Fugue in A

BWV 888

No. 19 from *Das wohltemperirte Clavier*, Part II

J. S. Bach
(1685–1750)

Bach completed Part II of *The Well-Tempered Clavier* in about 1742, roughly 20 years after the completion of Part I. As a double collection of preludes and fugues in all 24 keys, it was designed to demonstrate the full range of the tonal system at a time when the more remote keys were still little explored. The term 'well-tempered' indicates another aim of the collection: to advocate a system of tuning in which keys with numerous sharps or flats would be tolerable to the ear. Bach must have had in mind either today's equal temperament or else something fairly close to it. The title-page also makes it clear that the two books are designed for study by young players and for the enjoyment of those who are already proficient.

The Prelude in A from Part II, selected here, is a pastorale in three-part counterpoint. Much of it is a play on direct and inverted forms of the opening seven-note motif. The following fugue is also in three-part counterpoint, but it is very different in rhythm, with its witty dialogues between the on-the-beat dotted rhythms of the countersubjects and their offbeat equivalents in the subject itself (see, for example, b. 5).

Source: autograph MS, London, British Library, Add. MS 35021

Please turn the page for the music.

8

Prelude

[♩. = c.63]

Fugue

[♩ = c.80]

Fughetta

No. 4 from *Sieben Clavierstücke in Fughettenform*, Op. 126

Robert Schumann
(1810–56)

Sieben Clavierstücke in Fughettenform Seven Keyboard Pieces in Fughetta Form

Robert Schumann was a great admirer of the music of J. S. Bach: he strongly supported the creation of a Bach monument in Leipzig and the publication of a complete edition of his works. Schumann composed a set of Six Fugues, Op. 60, on the name BACH in 1845; and his advice to aspiring musicians was: 'Let *The Well-Tempered Clavier* be your daily bread. Then you will certainly become a solid musician.'

It is not surprising, then, that the figure of Bach lies behind the Op. 126 fughettas. The arresting opening motif of No. 4, selected here, includes the falling diminished 7th found in many of Bach's fugue subjects. The piece is a monothematic stretto fugue (i.e. with overlapping subject entries). After the opening exposition, strettos take place at the distance of one bar (b. 13), two bars (b. 19), and again one bar (b. 29). The conclusion (from b. 36) is largely restricted to the opening motif of the subject, whose entries are increasingly piled up on each other, creating the impression of a climactic close stretto.

Source: *Sieben Clavierstücke in Fughettenform*, Op. 126 (Elberfeld: F. W. Arnold, 1854)

B:1

Allegro

First movement from Sonata in B flat, Hob. XVI/41

Joseph Haydn
(1732–1809)

The Sonata in B flat, Hob. XVI/41, from which this movement is selected, belongs to a set of three sonatas that Haydn dedicated to Princess Marie of Liechtenstein, who had married into the family of his employer Prince Nicolaus Esterházy. The three sonatas were published as Haydn's Op. 37 in 1784, by which time the composer had already established an international reputation. His works of the 1780s, including this sonata, show increasing originality, freedom, humour and formal ingenuity.
Source: first edition, *Trois sonates pour le pianoforte*, Op. 37 (Speyer: Bossler, 1784)

Allegro molto e con brio

B:2

First movement from Sonata in C minor, Op. 10 No. 1

Edited by Barry Cooper

Ludwig van Beethoven
(1770–1827)

Beethoven's three Op. 10 piano sonatas belong to his early period in Vienna (1792–1802), when he established a reputation as a brilliant young pianist and composer by playing regularly in the homes of the Viennese aristocracy. Among his most generous patrons at that time was Countess Anna Margarete von Browne, to whom the Op. 10 sonatas were dedicated.

The first of the three works, whose opening Allegro is reproduced here, represents one of the earliest occurrences in Beethoven's piano music of the stormy, pathos-laden mood that he often associated with the key of C minor – the *Pathétique* Sonata, the Fifth Symphony, and the Op. 111 Piano Sonata are well-known examples.

Barry Cooper, editor of the ABRSM edition, says of the movement selected: 'The main theme…is characterized by two strongly contrasting motifs – the first fiery and aggressive, the second gentle and pleading. These contrasts permeate the rest of the movement…The distinction between semiquaver and demisemiquaver ornaments in bb. 11 and 13 is not significant (cf. the recapitulation, bb. 178 and 180, where they are reversed!).' In bb. 145–6 it would be sensible to make a drop in volume since another crescendo is about to begin. The edition printed here has broken slur lines to indicate editorial extensions of existing slurs.
Source: first edition, *Trois sonates pour le clavecin ou piano forte*, Op. 10 (Vienna, 1798)

Please turn the page for the music.

Allegro molto e con brio [♩. = c.63]

B:3

Minuet and Trio

Third movement from Sonata No. 1 in C, Op. 24

C. M. von Weber
(1786–1826)

Minuet

Allegro [♩. = c.66]

The German composer Carl Maria von Weber studied with Michael Haydn in Salzburg and with Georg Joseph Vogler in Vienna. In his mature years he held posts as director of the opera in Prague (1813–16) and Dresden (from 1817). Accordingly, his greatest achievements as a composer lie in the field of German opera – *Der Freischütz* and *Euryanthe*. However, from time to time he toured as a virtuoso pianist, and he composed four piano sonatas.

This Minuet and Trio from Sonata No. 1 in C, Op. 24 illustrates the early Romantic spirit and exuberant, dramatic style for which Weber is renowned. The parallel thirds in bb. 53–5 and 128–30 could be taken by both hands.

Source: *Grande sonate pour le pianoforte*, Op. 24 (Berlin: A. M. Schlesinger, 1812)

Trio
Poco ritenuto

Minuetto D.C.

Intermezzo in E flat

No. 1 from Three Intermezzos, Op. 117

Johannes Brahms
(1833–97)

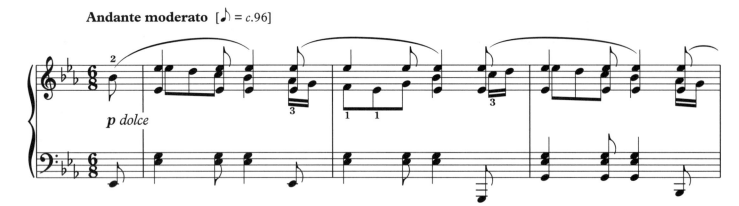

Johannes Brahms returned to the composition of piano music late in life – some years after the completion of his last orchestral works. Like Beethoven, he withdrew from the world of big public utterances into the private world of his innermost thoughts and feelings. Accordingly, the four late sets of short piano pieces, Opp. 116–19 of 1892–3, are among his most personal, intimate works.

The Three Intermezzos, Op. 117, of which the first is selected here, were composed and published in 1892. No. 1 is headed by an extract from the German poet Herder's translation of an anonymous Scottish poem, 'Lady Anne Bothwell's Lament'. An unhappy woman, deserted by the lover who fathered her child, sings the baby a lullaby, which in its original form reads:

> Balow, my babe, lie still and sleep!
> It grieves me sore to see thee weep.

Source: *Drei Intermezzi*, Op. 117 (Berlin: N. Simrock, 1892)

C:2

Prélude

First movement from *Suite bergamasque*

Moderato (tempo rubato) [♩ = *c*.96]

Claude Debussy
(1862–1918)

The French composer Claude Debussy entered the Paris Conservatoire in 1872, studying piano, theory and, later, composition. His mature piano music is regarded by many as the most original contribution to the repertory after Chopin.

The title *Suite bergamasque* perhaps alludes to a poem by the French poet Verlaine, rather than to the dance *bergamasca*. It is an early work, dating from around 1890, when Debussy was still writing in a late Romantic style. Hints of the subtle 'impressionist' manner with which he is chiefly associated are, however, occasionally heard – for example, in the episode that starts at b. 20 of *Prélude*, reproduced here. The four movements of the suite are *Prélude, Menuet*, the celebrated *Clair de lune*, and *Passepied*.

In *Prélude*, the sixth treble note of b. 2 reads *bb″* in the first edition, but in all parallel places (bb. 8, 67 and 73) it reads *a″*; the first bass note of b. 21 reads *f* in the first edition, but in all parallel places (bb. 20, 24, 25, etc.) it reads *a*.

Source: first edition, *Suite bergamasque* (Paris: E. Fromont, 1905)

poco rit.

C:3

Habanera

Ernesto Halffter
(1905–89)

The Spanish composer and conductor Ernesto Halffter studied for several years with Manuel de Falla, who remained a major influence on his compositions. Other influences included Ravel, with whom he also studied briefly, and Stravinsky. Halffter founded the Seville Conservatory in 1931.

The *habanera* is a 19th-century Cuban dance and song, named after the capital city Havana. It is in a very moderate duple time and is based on a distinctive dotted rhythm. This popular genre made its way into the classical repertoire, and by the end of the 19th century, composers such as Bizet, Chabrier, Massenet and Saint-Saëns had all incorporated it into compositions, most famously Bizet in his opera *Carmen*.

In Halffter's 20th-century *habanera*, the hypnotically repeating ostinato rhythm in the left hand and the dreamy melody that plays over it combine to evoke the heat and laziness of a Mediterranean afternoon. The unusual notation in bb. 1–4 tells the pianist to use the pedal to sustain the minim notes for the whole bar. *A tempo* in the first- and second-time bars (at b. 36) indicates a return to strict dance time, which might suggest a certain *tempo rubato* in the preceding paragraph (from b. 20).

Allegro

First movement from Sonatina, Op. 1 No. 1

C:4

Arvo Pärt
(born 1935)

The Estonian composer Arvo Pärt studied at the Tallinn Conservatory, graduating in 1963. During that time he also worked as a sound producer for Estonian Radio (1957–67). He moved to Berlin in the 1980s. His early music, such as the sonatina of 1958, from which this movement is selected, was neo-classical in style and owes much to Prokofiev.

In this Allegro, a two-part *Spielfuge* (bb. 1 and 47) – a type of fugue in which emphasis is laid on manual dexterity – alternates with a grandly homophonic, lyrical episode (bb. 19 and 85). Although the composer's metronome mark is ♩ = 126, students may prefer a more relaxed tempo of ♩ = c.104. Either tempo would be acceptable in the exam.

Hallelujah Time

Oscar Peterson
(1925–2007)

The Canadian jazz pianist and composer Oscar Peterson formed a trio for piano, guitar and double bass in the early 1950s. He began to perform regularly as a solo pianist in the early 1970s, and over the years he appeared with many of the leading jazz musicians of his day, including Ella Fitzgerald, Stan Getz, Dizzie Gillespie and Billie Holiday. Owing to his remarkable technique and range of style, he is widely regarded as one of the finest jazz pianists of the later 20th century.

In this piece, although the composer's metronome mark is ♩ = 126, students may prefer a tempo of ♩ = *c*.108. Either tempo would be acceptable in the exam.

Poème

No. 2 from *Deux poèmes*, Op. 69

A. N. Skryabin
(1872–1915)

The Russian composer and pianist Aleksandr Nikolayevich Skryabin studied at the Moscow Conservatory from 1888 to 1892, after which he embarked on a successful career as a concert pianist, playing mainly his own music and that of Chopin. He taught at the Moscow Conservatory from 1898 to 1902 and then moved to Western Europe, not returning to Russia till 1909. His music is written in a very personal and highly chromatic, post-Wagnerian style.

The *Deux poèmes*, Op. 69, of which the second is selected here, belong to Skryabin's late Russian period, when he also composed the last five of his ten piano sonatas.

Source: *Deux poèmes pour piano*, Op. 69 (Moscow and Leipzig: P. Jurgenson, 1913)